C0-AYJ-268

Selected Stories
from
Panchatantra

Compiled by
'KUNWAR' ANIL KUMAR

MANOJ PUBLICATIONS

CONTENTS

❏ THE FALCON AND THE CROW — 3

❏ THE LOUSE AND THE BED-BUG — 4

❏ THE SHEPHERD AND THE WOLF — 6

❏ HELLO! CAVE — 8

❏ THE BEAR AND GOLU AND MOLU — 10

❏ THE KING COBRA AND THE ANTS — 12

❏ THE KING AND THE PARROTS — 14

❏ THE DHOBI'S DONKEY — 16

❏ THE BULLOCK AND THE LION — 17

❏ THE FOOLISH MONKEY AND THE KING — 20

❏ THE CROW AND THE MONKEY — 22

❏ THE MONKEYS AND THE RED BERRIES — 24

❏ THE TRICK OF THE CROW — 26

❏ THE LITTLE MICE AND THE BIG ELEPHANTS — 29

❏ THE LION AND THE WOODCUTTER — 32

❏ THE WISE CRAB — 35

❏ THE HERMIT AND THE JUMPING RAT — 38

❏ THE MONKEY AND THE LOG — 40

© *All Rights Reserved*

Under the Indian Copyright Act, all rights of the contents and photographs of this book are reserved with M/s. Manoj Publications, 761, Main Road Burari, Delhi-84. Therefore, no part of this book including the name, title, design, inside matter or photographs be reproduced or copied in any form or by any means, in full or in part, in any language. Breach of this condition is liable to legal action and fine.

All disputes subject to Delhi Jurisdiction.

Manoj Publications

761, Main Road Burari, Delhi-110084

Phone : 27611116, 27611349

Fax : 27611546, *Mobile :* 9868112194

E-mail : manojpublications @vsnl.net

Website : www.manojpublications.com

ISBN : 81-8133-401-9

Showroom :

1583-84, Dariba Kalan,
Chandani Chowk, Delhi-6

Phone : 23262174, 23268216
Mobile : 9818753569

Printers :
Jain Offset Printers

THE FALCON AND THE CROW

THERE lived a big falcon on a high mountain rock. Down in the plains, there lived a black crow in a huge tree.

One day, the falcon swooped down upon a rabbit on the ground. The falcon caught hold of the rabbit in his talons and flew back to his nest on the mountain rock.

The black crow saw the falcon do this thrilling feat. He thought to perform the same feat himself.

'What a fun it was to watch the falcon pick up the rabbit from the ground! Now I'll myself do this.' The crow thought to himself and flew high in the sky. Then, he swooped down with great force upon a rabbit sitting on the ground. But his swoop was not correctly aimed at and instead of catching the rabbit, he dashed against a heavy rock. His head cracked and died on the spot.

Moral—*Never imitate others in a foolish manner.*

THE LOUSE AND THE BED-BUG

THERE lived a white louse named Mandarisarpini in the spacious bedroom of a mighty king. She used to live in the corner of the bedsheet spread over the king's beautiful bedstead. Everyday, when the king was fast asleep, the louse sipped his blood and crept back again into a corner of the bed-cover to hide herself.

One night, a bed-bug named Agnimukha strolled into the bedroom of the king. The louse saw him and told to get out since the whole of the bedroom was her territory only. But the bed-bug said to her cleverly, "Look, you ought to be a little courteous to your guests. I'm your guest tonight." The louse got carried away by the bed-bug's sweet talks. She gave him shelter saying, "It's all right. You can stay here tonight. But, you will not bite the king to suck his blood."

"But I'm your guest. Give me some eatables?" the bed-bug asked. "What better food you can serve me than the king's blood."

"Well!", replied the louse. "You can suck the king's blood silently. He must not get hurt in anyway."

"Agreed", said the clever bed-bug and waited for the king to arrive in the bedroom and sleep on the bed.

When the night fell, the king entered into his bedroom and slept on the bed.

The greedy bed-bug forgot all about his promises and bit the sleeping king hard to suck his blood.

"It's a royal blood", thought the bed-bug and continued sucking till the king felt a terrible itching in his skin. The king woke up and then ordered his servants to find the bed-bug and kill it.

But the bed-bug hid himself into the joints of the bed-stead and thus escaped his detection. The servants of the king, instead, found the louse on the bedsheet. They caught her and killed.

Moral—*Never trust the strangers.*

THE SHEPHERD AND THE WOLF

THERE lived a shepherd in a village. He had many sheep. He took them out every morning for grazing. One day, his wife fell ill and he had to go to the city to purchase some medicines for his ailing wife. 'There will be no one to take care of the sheep', he thought to himself. Then he called his son and told him, "Ramu, I'm going to the city to purchase some medicines for your mother. It will take me two or three days to come back. So take care of the sheep. Save them from being attacked by the tigers and wolves. There are many wild animals in the nearby forest. They might kill our sheep."

Ramu listened the advice carefully and the next day, he left for the nearby hillside with his flock of sheep. But Ramu was a mischievous boy. He was feeling lonely. So he wanted to have some fun. He stood on a high rock and began shouting "Wolf! wolf!, help."

The villagers heard Ramu crying for help. They ran towards the hillside to help the boy, carrying big sticks in their hands. When they reached there they found that there was no wolf. The sheep were grazing happily and the shepherd boy was playing on a flute.

"Where is the wolf?" the villagers asked the boy.

"There is no wolf here. I was joking," the boy said and laughed.

The villagers became very angry and returned to their work.

Next day, the boy played the same trick. The villagers again reached there to help the boy. But when they came to know that the boy was lying, they felt highly annoyed and went back to the village cursing the boy.

But on the third day, a wolf really came there. The boy got frightened to see his red eyes. The wolf was huffing and growling. He began advancing towards the flock of sheep, gnashing his teeth and lolling his tongue. The boy lost his courage and began trembling with fear. He shouted, "Wolf, wolf, please help!" But to no avail.

This time no one came to help him. The villagers thought that Ramu was upto his old tricks. The wolf killed many sheep of Ramu. Ramu returned home weeping.

Moral—*People do not trust a liar.*

HELLO! CAVE

LONG ago, there lived a lion named Kharanakhara. He had been trying to hunt for his prey for the last two days, but could not succeed due to his old age and physical infirmity. He was no longer strong to hunt for his food. He was quite dejected and disappointed. He thought that he would die of strarving. One day, while he was wandering in the jungle, he came across a cave. 'There must be some animal who lives in this cave'; so thought the lion. 'I will hide myself inside it and wait for its occupant to enter. And as soon as the occupant enters the cave, I shall kill him and eat his flesh.' Thinking thus, the lion entered the cave and hid himself carefully.

After sometime, a fox came near the cave. The cave belonged to her. The fox was surprised to find the foot-marks of a lion pointing towards the cave. 'Some lion has stealthily entered my cave', he thought to himself. But to make sure of the presence of the lion inside the cave, the fox played upon a trick.

The fox stood at some distance from the cave to save himself in case of a sudden attack and shouted, "Hello cave! I've come back. Speak to me as you have been doing earlier. Why're you keeping silent? May I come in and occupy my residence?"

Hearing the fox calling the cave, the lion thought to himself, that the cave he was hiding in, must in reality be a talking cave. The cave might be keeping quiet because of his kingly presence inside. Therefore, if the cave didn't answer to the fox's question, the fox might go away to occupy some other cave and thus, he would have to go without a meal once again.

Trying to be wise, the lion answered in a roaring voice on behalf of the cave, "I've not forgotten my practice of speaking to you when you come, my dear fox. Come in and be at home."

Thus, the clever fox confirmed the presence of the lion hiding in his cave and ran away without losing a single moment, saying, "Only a fool would believe that a cave speaks."

Moral—*Presence of mind is the best weapon to guard oneself in every sphere of life.*

THE BEAR AND GOLU AND MOLU

GOLU and Molu were fast friends. Golu was lean and thin, whereas Molu was fat. People, in the village laughed at this combination. For a major period of the day, they would be seen together. Everyone admired their friendship. Once, they got an invitation from one of their friends, who had invited them to attend his sister's marriage. The marriage was to take place in a nearby village.

But in order to reach the village, one had to pass through a forest, which was full of wild animals like tigers and bears etc.

While walking through the forest, Golu and Molu saw a bear coming towards them. Both of them got frightened. Golu who was lean and skinny, ran towards a big tree and climbed on it. Poor Molu being fat could not run fast and climb up the tree. But he showed his presence of mind. He had heard that bears did not eat dead bodies. So he lay down still on the ground and held his breath for a while, feighning himself dead. The bear came near Molu growling. He sniffed at his face and body. He took Molu to be a dead body and went away.

When the bear had gone away, Golu climbed down the tree. He went to Molu and asked, "I saw the bear talking to you. What did he say to you, my friend?"

"Don't call me a friend", said Molu. "And that is what the bear also told me. He said, 'Don't trust Golu. He is not your friend."

Golu was very ashamed. He felt sorry to have left his friend alone when in danger. Thus, their friendship ended for ever.

Moral—*A friend in need is a friend indeed.*

THE KING COBRA AND THE ANTS

THERE lived a big king cobra in a dense forest. As usual, he fed on birds' eggs, lizards, frogs and other small creatures. The whole night he hunted the small creatures and when the day broke, he went into his hole to sleep. Gradually, he became fat. And his fat grew to such a measure that it became difficult for him to enter and come out of his hole without being scratched.

Ultimately, he decided to abandon his hole and selected a huge tree for his new home. But there was an ant hill at the root of the tree. It was impossible for king cobra to put up with the ants. So, he went to the ant hill and said, "I'm the king of this forest. I order all of you to go from this place and live somewhere else."

There were other animals, too, around. They began trembling with fear to see such a huge snake before them. They ran for their lives. But the ants paid no heed to his threats. Thousands of ants streamed out of the ant hill. Soon they were swarming all over the body of the king cobra, stinging and biting him. Thousands of thorny pricks all over his body caused unbearable pain to him. The king cobra tried to keep the ants away, but in vain. He wriggled in pain and at last, died a painful death.

Moral—*Even the strong and mighty cannot face the small ones, when in a large number, at a time.*

THE KING AND THE PARROTS

ONCE a tribal king went to a jungle to hunt for birds. While hunting, he caught two parrots in his net. He was happy to catch the parrots as he could teach them to talk and then let his children play with the talking parrots.

But while the tribal king was returning home with his parrots, one of the parrots escaped from the net and flew away. The tribal king chased the parrot, but the parrot disappeared in the sky.

The tribal king brought the other parrot home and taught it to speak like him. Soon the parrot learnt to talk like a tribal man.

The other parrot which had managed to escape, was caught by a sage. The sage taught the parrot to recite holy hymns.

The sage lived at one end of the jungle, while the tribal king lived at the other end.

One day, a king of a nearby kingdom came in the jungle riding a horse. When he approached the tribal king's house the parrot shouted from inside the cage hanging outside the house, "Here comes someone. Catch this fellow and beat him thoroughly."

The king hearing the parrot speak in such a filthy manner, left that place and reached the other end of the jungle where the sage lived. The sage's parrot was also kept in a cage, which was hanging outside the sage's cottage.

As soon as the parrot saw the king approaching the cottage it said, "Welcome! Please come in and have a seat. What can I do for you? Have a glass of water. Eat some sweets."

After having welcomed him properly with all the etiquettes, the parrot called his master, "Guruji, here comes a guest on his horseback. Take him inside and offer him a seat. Serve him food."

The king was highly impressed with this intelligent talking parrot. He was quick to understand that good environment and training always yield a better result.

The tribal king's parrot spoke rudely, while the sage's parrot greeted him in a polite tone.

Moral—*A man is known by the company he keeps.*

THE DHOBI'S DONKEY

ONCE upon a time, there lived a dhobi in a village. He had a donkey and a dog as his pets. The dog guarded his master's house and accompanied him wherever he went. The donkey used to carry the load of clothes. The dhobi loved his dog very much. And the dog, whenever, he saw his master, would bark a little and wag his tail. He would raise his front legs and put them on the chest of his master. Dhobi would pat his dog in return, for his loving gesture.

This made the donkey jealous. He cursed his ill-fate; 'What a bad luck I've. My master doesn't love me in spite of my hard labour. Now, I must do what this dog does to please my master.'

So, the next time, when he saw his master coming, he ran towards him. He brayed a little and tried to wag his tail. He raised his front legs and put them on his master's body.

The dhobi got frightened to see his donkey's abnormal behaviour. He thought that the donkey might have gone crazy. So he picked up a lathi and beat up the donkey till it fell on the ground.

Moral—*Jealousy is harmful.*

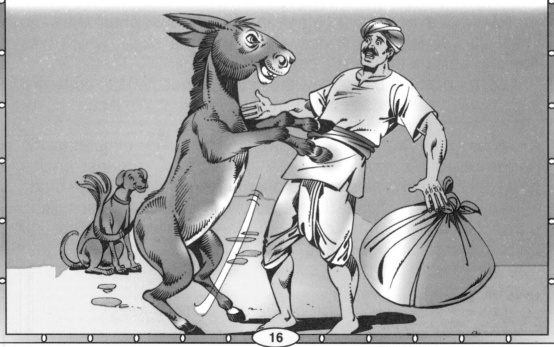

16

THE BULLOCK AND THE LION

ONCE upon a time, a village merchant named Vardhmanaka, was going to Mathura town on his bullock cart. Two bullocks—Sanjeevaka and Nandaka were pulling the bullock cart.

While the merchant's cart was moving along the bank of the river Yamuna, Sanjeevaka, all of a sudden, stepped into a swampy spot. He tried to come out of the swamp, but couldn't succeed. The merchant too tried his level best to pull out Sanjeevaka from the swamp, but to no avail. Ultimately he had to leave Sanjeevaka there and proceed on with his onward journey.

Sanjeevaka thought, "How I have served my master so loyally throughout my life and how my master has repaid my loyalty."

Now, Sanjeevaka was left to his fate. The only alternative he had—either resign to fate and die in the swamp or fight till the end. Sanjeevaka gathered up courage. He began applying his enormous muscle power. There is a saying—'God helps those who help themselves.' At last after great effort, he managed to wriggle his way out of the swamp.

Now, as he had nowhere to go and he didn't want to return to his master's house, he started moving along the banks of the river. He ate green grass in the nearby forest and drank fresh water from the river. Soon he became healthy and stout. He started bellowing like a lion. His thunder like bellowing could be heard miles away.

Once, king lion whose name was Pingalaka, came to the river to drink water. Suddenly, he heard thunder-like bellowing. He got frightened and ran away into his cave.

King lion had two jackals named Damnaka and Kartaka as his ministers. When Damnaka came to know that some kind of fear had overpowered his king, he asked him, "Your Majesty, tell me who is he you are afraid of? I'll bring him to you."

The lion was not ready to admit the fact, but after great hesitation, he told the real cause of his fear. Damnaka assured king lion that he will find out the actual source of the thundering sound.

Soon Damnaka brought Sanjeevaka to the court of his king. "Your Majesty, this is the animal, who has been making the thundering sound. He says that Lord Shiva has sent him to roam about in our kingdom."

King lion was very pleased. Soon he became friendly with him. He spent much of his time chatting with Sanjeevaka.

Gradually, king lion became very spiritual. He stopped killing his preys and even neglected his kingdom. This worried Damnaka and Kartaka and the other animals of the jungle.

Damnaka thought of a plan to solve the problem. He went to king lion and said, "Your Majesty, Sanjeevaka has an evil eye on your kingdom. He wants to kill you and become the king himself."

And the next day, Damnaka went to Sanjeevaka and told him a different story. "King lion has a plan to kill you and distribute your flesh to all other animals of the jungle. Better you kill king lion with your pointed horns, before he kills you."

Sanjeevaka became very angry to hear Damnaka's words. He went to the court of king lion and started bellowing in a thundering tone. This annoyed king lion and he pounced upon Sanjeevaka with a thundering roar.

Both were strong...they engaged themselves in a fierce fight. Sanjeevaka tried to kill king lion with his pointed horns, but in vain. King lion killed Sanjeevaka with his sharp claws and ate his flesh.

Though king lion killed Sanjeevaka but he felt very sad. After all, Sanjeevaka was once his friend. But since, Damnaka had convinced him that Sanjeevaka was a traitor, he had to act upon his advice. Later, he made Damnaka the chief minister of his kingdom.

Moral—*Never befriend a natural enemy.*

THE FOOLISH MONKEY & THE KING

LONG, long ago, there lived a king, who was very fond of monkeys. One big monkey used to serve the king as his personal attendant. The king considered him to be as intelligent as a human being. When the king took rest in his bedroom, the monkey used to sit beside him like his personal bodyguard.

Once the king returned to his palace after many days. He had gone to a nearby forest for hunting animals and birds. Despite best arrangements by his ministers for his comfort in the forest, he had an uncomfortable life, if compared with the comforts that he was used to in his palace. So, he went to bed early. He told the monkey to keep a watch around and see that nobody disturbed him during his sleep. The monkey sat near king's bed with a naked sword in his hand and started guarding his master.

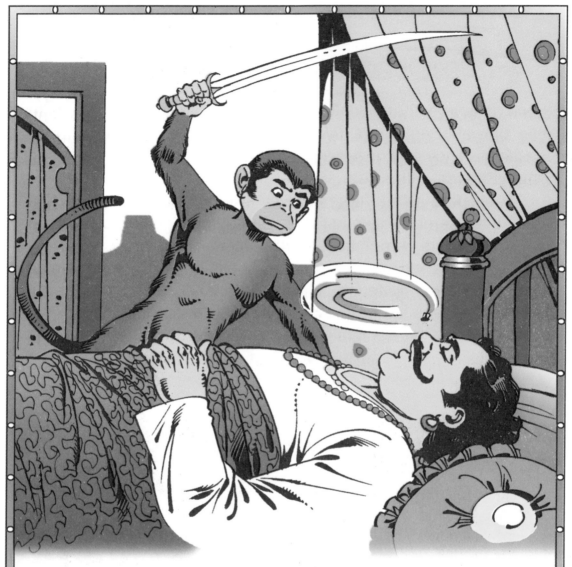

After sometime, the monkey heard a small fly buzzing around in the room. The fly soon came nearer and sat on the face of the sleeping king.

The monkey first tried to shoo away the fly, but it kept on hovering over the king's face. It sat on his nose again and again. Seeing this the monkey lost his temper. He decided to kill the fly. So, when the fly sat on the king's nose again, the monkey hit it with the sword. The fly flew away, but the sword fell on king's neck and he was beheaded. He died then and there on his bed.

Moral—*A wise enemy is better than a foolish friend.*

THE CROW AND THE MONKEY

Long, long ago, there was a big banyan tree in a dense jungle. In this banyan tree, there lived a crow's family happily, with its nestlings. They had a beautiful and strong nest on a thick and sturdy branch of the tree.

There was also a huge monkey living in the banyan tree. He had no house of his own to live in. Sometimes, he would sleep on one branch and sometimes, on the other.

Once it started raining very heavily. The rain was accompanied with thunder and lightening. Strong cold winds blew. There was not an inch of space left on the ground which was not lashed by the rain. While the crow's family protected itself from the fury of the rain by taking shelter inside the nest, the monkey could not find any safe place for himself. He began to shiver badly with cold.

The crow seeing the monkey in such a pitiable condition said to him, "Poor fellow. Even though you are stout and healthy, you never built a house for yourself. Look at us. We have a strong nest to protect ourselves from the fury of the rain and storm. Why don't you build a house for yourself, instead of wandering around aimlessly and shifting from one branch to the other in a lazy manner? God has given you two hands; make use of them."

The monkey, hearing the crow's words became very annoyed. He said, "You foolish black crow, how dare you advise me, and teach me the do's and don'ts of my life. You have lost your sense of etiquettes. I must teach you, how to behave." Saying so, the monkey tore off a branch from the tree and began to beat at the crow's nest. Soon the nest was broken into pieces. The nestlings fell down upon the rain soaked ground and died. The crows somehow flew away and took shelter on some other branch. They wept bitterly over their young ones' death. They had no time even to repent for their good intentioned advice given to the monkey.

Moral—*It's better not to advise others in their personal matters.*

THE MONKEYS AND THE RED BERRIES

LONG, long ago, there lived a troop of monkeys in a hilly region. When winter fell, the monkeys began to shiver with cold. They had no place to protect themselves. One of the monkeys suggested that they should go to the nearby village and take shelter in the houses of human beings till the winter lasted. His suggestion was accepted by all the monkeys. All of them shifted from the hilly region to an adjoining village.

But, next morning, when the villagers saw a big troop of monkeys, all of a sudden, jumping from branches to branches and on their roof-tops, they greeted them by pelting stones and showing sticks.

Thus, the monkeys, instead of getting shelter in the village, were compelled to retreat to the hilly region and face the chilly winds and the snowfalls once again.

Then, ultimately one of the monkeys thought of making a fire to warm up the surrounding. He had seen the villagers sitting around fire and warming up themselves. There were some red berry trees around. The monkeys mistook them for burning coals. They plucked those berries and placed them under a pile of dry sticks. They tried to make a fire by blowing into the pile. But there was no fire. The monkeys became sad.

There were also a few birds who lived in the same tree where the monkeys lived. Seeing the plight of the monkeys, one of the birds said to them, "What a fool you are, trying to make fire from those red fruits. Have the fruits ever made fire? Why don't all of you take shelter in the nearby cave?"

When the monkeys saw the birds advising them they became red with rage. One old monkey said, "You dare call us fools. Why do you poke your nose into our affairs?"

But the little bird kept on chirping and advising the monkeys. Then one huge monkey caught hold of the neck of that noisy bird and dashed it against the tree trunk. The bird died on the spot.

Moral—*It's no use advising idiots. Instead, it might create more troubles.*

THE TRICK OF THE CROW

ONCE upon a time, there stood a huge peepal tree on the outskirts of a small village. In this tree there lived a pair of crows with their young ones. And at the root of the tree there lived a big black serpent in a deep hole. Every time the crows laid their eggs, the serpent crept up the tree and ate all the eggs and the young ones. With the result, the crows were never able to raise their young ones. This made the crows very sad. They didn't know how to get rid of the killer serpent.

One day, the crows went to a fox. The fox was their friend.

"Hello dear friends, come in", said the fox seeing the crows at his door, "You two seem to be very sad. What's the matter?"

"The root cause of our problem is a black serpent. He is after us. He eats up our eggs and the young ones. Please help us get rid of this bloody serpent," said the female crow to the fox.

The fox too was shocked and promised to help. She thought for a few minutes and then laid out a plan before the crows.

"Listen carefully", said the fox, "you know where the king's palace is situated. You've also seen the queen taking bath in an open swimming pool, inside the palace. The queen, while taking bath always removes all her ornaments and keeps them on a tray kept by the side of the pool. While she is busy taking her bath, you two swoop down upon the tray and pick up two diamond ornaments from it. Drop them into the serpent's hole. The servants of the queen will come chasing you and finding the ornaments into the serpent's hole, they will first kill the serpent to save them from being bitten by it and then will take the ornaments out of the hole. Thus, the serpent will be killed and you too will be saved from all the troubles of killing it by yourself."

This was a very bright idea. The crows liked it. They flew to the king's palace. There they saw the queen taking bath in a swimming pool. She had removed her ornaments and kept them in a tray. The crows swooped down upon the tray, picked up two expensive diamond necklaces from it and flew towards the snake's hole. The guards ran after the crows brandishing their sticks and swords. They chased the crows and soon reached that big peepal tree, where the big black snake lived. They found the diamond necklaces, lying inside the serpent's hole. Afraid of the snake, they first killed the snake by sticks and swords and then took out the ornaments and returned to the palace.

The crows thanked the fox for his help and lived happily in the peepal tree, thereafter.

Moral—*Intelligence is greater than strength.*

THE LITTLE MICE AND THE BIG ELEPHANTS

ONCE upon a time a village was devastated by a strong earthquake. Damaged houses and roads could be seen everywhere. The village was, as a matter of fact, in a total ruin. The villagers had abandoned their houses and had settled in a nearby village. Finding the place totally devoid of residents, the mice began to live in the ruined houses. Soon their number grew into thousands and millions.

There was also a big lake situated near the ruined village. A herd of elephants used to visit the lake for drinking water. The herd had no other way but to pass through the ruins of the village to reach the lake. While on their way, the elephants trampled hundreds of mice daily under their heavy feet. This made all the mice very sad. Many of them were killed while a large number of them were maimed.

In order to find a solution to this problem, the mice held a meeting. In the meeting, it was decided that a request should be made to the king of elephants to this effect. The king of mice met the king of elephants and said to him, "Your Majesty, we live in the ruins of the village, but everytime your herd crosses the village, thousands of my subjects get trampled under the massive feet of your herd. Kindly change your route. If you do so, we promise to help you in the hour of your need."

Hearing this the king of elephants laughed. "You rats are so tiny to be of any help to giants like us. But in any case, we would do a favour to all of you by changing our route to reach the lake and to make you more safe." The king of mice thanked the king elephant and returned home.

After sometime, the king of a nearby kingdom thought of increasing the number of elephants in his army. He ordered his soldiers to catch more elephants for this purpose.

The king's soldiers saw this herd and put a strong net around the elephants. The elephants got trapped. They struggled hard to free themselves, but in vain.

Suddenly, the king of elephants recollected the promise of the king of mice, who had earlier talked about helping the elephants when needed. So he trumpeted loudly to call the king of mice. The king of mice hearing the voice of the king of elephants immediately rushed along with his followers to rescue the herd. There he found the elephants trapped in a thick net.

The mice set themselves on the task. They bit off the thick net at thousands of spots making it loose. The elephants broke the loose net and freed themselves.

They thanked the mice for their great help and extended their hands of friendship to them forever.

Moral—*Sometimes a weak looking person may prove stronger than others.*

THE LION AND THE WOODCUTTER

THERE lived a lion in a dense forest. He had two good friends, a crow and a jackal. The lion hunted the whole day for his prey. And after assuaging his hunger, he gave the remaining food to his friends. The jackal and the crow were very happy to eat free food. They ate their fill and lazed around since they did not have to exert themselves to earn their food.

In the nearby village, there lived a woodcutter and his wife. Both were went to the forest to collect wood and returned home after hours of hard work. When they returned, the woodcutter's wife cooked meals and they both ate sitting in front of their house.

Once the lion saw the woodcutter and his wife sitting outside their house and eating tasty meals. He could get the smell of the food from quite a distance. He went near them. The woodcutter and his wife, instead of running away from the spot, very courageously welcomed the lion and asked him to take a seat

beside them. The lion was surprised. He sat beside the couple and happily ate the meals offered by the woodcutter. The lion was very pleased to see the hospitality extended by them and he was all-the-more pleased to eat and enjoy cooked meals. This was for the first time that he got the taste of cooked meals, otherwise he had always had raw meals in the past. While returning to the forest the lion thanked the woodcutter and his wife for the tasty food.

The woodcutter's wife said to the lion, "You're always welcome. Please do come everyday and share the food with us."

Once again the lion was astonished. This kind of behaviour was uncommon among them. The animals would never offer food to others; rather, they would snatch each other's food and injure each other in the process.

The lion bowed before them with respect and went away. He took his lunch the next day also with the woodcutter's family. Gradually, he forgot to hunt for his prey and became lazy.

This change in the lion's habits was a matter of worry for his friends, the jackal and the crow. In fact, his friends had to go

hungry as they no longer got the left-overs of the lion's food. They decided to find the reason in his friend's attitude. So both of them decided to keep a watch on the lion's activities.

One day, they saw the lion sitting beside the woodcutter and his wife and having a good meal. They decided to meet the lion on the spot. But as soon as the woodcutter and his wife saw the jackal and the crow, they climbed up a nearby tall tree.

Seeing them running away the lion asked surprisingly, "What's the matter? Why do you run away, I won't harm you."

The woodcutter replied, "We're not afraid of you. It's actually your two friends who frighten us. We trust you, but not your cunning friends. We have known them and their habits for a long time. They may prove more dangerous than you."

The lion was very disheartened to listen to this. He warned his friends not to meet him again.

Moral—*Beware of cunning people.*

THE WISE CRAB

THERE stood two big banyan trees, side by side, in a dense forest. In fact, they were at such a short distance from each other that they formed one huge banyan tree. Thousands of cranes lived in this tree. In a deep hole in its trunk, also lived a big black snake.

The snake used to climb up the tree to its branches and eat the baby cranes from their nests, when their parents were away in search of food.

This had become a daily routine, unfortunate cranes were the soft targets. Every evening, on return to their nests, the hapless cranes would find their nestlings missing, and they were so helpless that they could not do anything to get rid of the snake.

One day, a crab saw some cranes standing by the side of the lake and weeping bitterly. When he asked them the reason, the cranes said, "There's a big black snake living in the tree. Everyday he eats up our babies. We don't know how to get rid of him."

The crab thought to himself that the cranes too were crabs' enemies. They ate crabs' babies. Why not give the cranes an idea which not only would kill the snake but finish the cranes also.

So, the crab said, "Don't weep. I've an idea which will help kill the snake."

"Yes, please help us," requested the cranes.

"There is a big mongoose living at a little distance from the banyan trees. You put a few fish all along the path running from the mongoose's hole to the banyan tree. The mongoose will eat the fish one by one and then reach the snake's hole. Now you can yourself imagine, what will happen thereafter."

The cranes became very happy to get such a brilliant idea. They acted according to the plan.

36

Thereafter, the mongoose ate up all the fish put all along the path leading up to his home and then reached the banyan tree. There he found the snake in the hole. A fierce fighting took place between them and the mongoose killed the snake.

But instead of going back to his hole after killing the serpent , the mongoose further climbed up the tree and started eating the baby cranes, one by one. Soon the mongoose ate up all the baby cranes living in the banyan tree.

After eating a large number of baby cranes, the mongoose became very fat and lazy. One day, while he was sleeping on a branch of the tree, he slipped and fell on to the ground and died then and there.

Moral—*Never act hastily on your enemy's advice.*

THE HERMIT AND THE JUMPING RAT

On the outskirts of a small village, there was a temple, in which, there lived a pundit. He used to perform pooja in the nearby villages. In the evening, after he had finished his meals, he would keep the remaining food, if any, into a bowl. He would hang the bowl upon a hook, which was attached to the ceiling by a string.

There, in the same temple, lived a fat rat. He was so fat that he didn't fear even the cats. He would come out of his hole during the night time and jump over to the hanging bowl and eat whatever food available in it. The next morning, when pundit would open the bowl, he would find it empty. This went on daily. The pundit became very sad. He didn't know how to drive the rat away from the temple.

Once a hermit from another village came to stay with the pundit. The pundit had no food to offer to his guest. He became embarrassed and talked about his problem with the hermit.

"Don't worry", said the hermit. "We must find the hole where the rat lives and destroy it. The rat must have stored a large quantity of food in the hole. It's this hoard's smell that gives strength to the rat to make high jumps and reach the food bowl."

So the pundit and the hermit together traced the rat's hole. They dug it up and destroyed the food stock stored there by the rat.

The rat became frustrated to see his food stock destroyed. He lost his vital energy to make high jumps. He had to go hungry now. He became weak due to hunger and left the temple in search of food. While he was running around in search of food a hungry cat spotted him. The cat pounced upon him and killed him.

Moral—*The wealth does give strength.*

THE MONKEY AND THE LOG

ONCE some monkeys were sitting in a tree. The tree was at such a place, where construction of a temple was going on. A carpenter was sawing a huge log to cut it into two parts. Just then the bell rang for the lunch break. He pushed a wedge into the split portion of the half sawed log and went for lunch, along with other workers.

When the monkeys saw that there was nobody around, they jumped down from the tree and came near the temple. They began to play with the tools lying there. One of the monkeys, who was very curious about all those things, went round the half sawed log. Then sat on top of it. He spread his legs on both sides of the log, whereas his tail dangled through the split portion.

Now the monkey started prying the wedge out of the log. Suddenly, it came out. The split parts of the log firmly snapped shut together crushing the monkeys tail in between. The monkey cried in pain and jumped off the log, but his tail was cut off for ever.

Moral—*Look before you leap.*